Traditional Carol Book

All the favourites for carol singers, choirs, organists, pianists and keyboard players

We hope you enjoy the music in this book.
Further copies are available
from your local music shop or Christian bookshop.

In case of difficulty, please contact the publisher direct by writing to:

The Sales Department
KEVIN MAYHEW LTD
Buxhall
Stowmarket
Suffolk
IP14 3DJ

Phone 01449 737978
Fax 01449 737834

Please ask for our complete catalogue of outstanding Church Music

First published in Great Britain in 1996 by Kevin Mayhew Ltd.

ISBN 0 86209 856 4
Catalogue No: 1450053

1 2 3 4 5 6 7 8 9

Front Cover: *Madonna and Child* by Julius Schnorr von Carolsfeld.
Courtesy of Christie's Images. Reproduced by kind permission.
Cover design by Graham Johnstone and Veronica Ward.

Music Editor: Geoffrey Moore
Music setting by Daniel Kelly and Geoffrey Moore

Printed and bound in Great Britain

Contents

1 Good King Wenceslas

TEMPUS ADEST FLORIDUM 76 76 D

2. 'Hither, page, and stand by me,
   if thou know'st it, telling,
   yonder peasant, who is he,
   where and what his dwelling?'
   'Sire, he lives a good league hence,
   underneath the mountain,
   right against the forest fence,
   by Saint Agnes' fountain.'

3. 'Bring me flesh, and bring me wine,
   bring me pine logs hither:
   thou and I will see him dine,
   when we bring them thither.'
   Page and monarch, forth they went,
   forth they went together;
   through the rude wind's wild lament,
   and the bitter weather.

4. 'Sire, the night is darker now,
   and the wind blows stronger;
   fails my heart, I know not how;
   I can go no longer.'
   'Mark my footsteps good, my page;
   tread thou in them boldly:
   thou shalt find the winter's rage
   freeze thy blood less coldly.'

5. In his master's steps he trod,
   where the snow lay dinted;
   heat was in the very sod
   which the Saint had printed.
   Therefore, Christians all, be sure,
   wealth or rank possessing,
   ye who now will bless the poor,
   shall yourselves find blessing.

Text: John Mason Neale (1818 - 1866) alt.
Music: from *Piae Cantiones* (1582) arr. John Stainer (1840 - 1901)

2 O come, all ye faithful

ADESTE FIDELES Irregular and Refrain

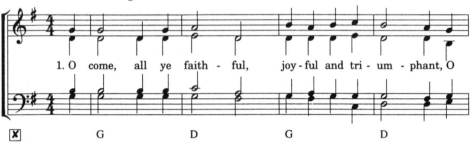

1. O come, all ye faith - ful, joy - ful and tri - um - phant, O

G   D   G   D

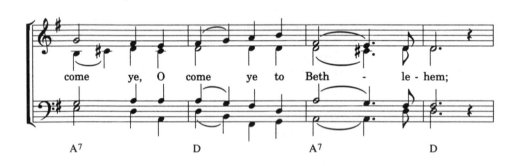

come ye, O come ye to Beth - le - hem;

A⁷   D   A⁷   D

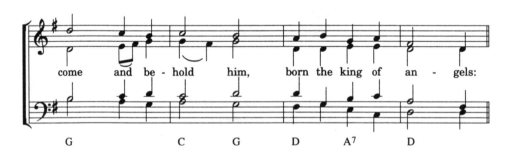

come and be - hold him, born the king of an - gels:

G   C   G   D   A⁷   D

Refrain

O come,
O come, let us a - dore him, O come, let us a - dore him, O

G   G⁷

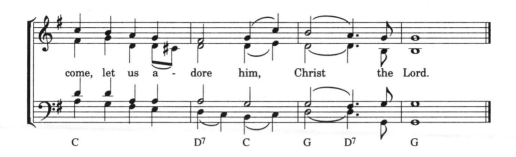

come, let us a - dore him, Christ the Lord.

C   D⁷ C   G   D⁷   G

2. God of God,
   Light of Light,
   lo, he abhors not the Virgin's womb;
   very God, begotten not created:

3. See how the shepherds,
   summoned to his cradle,
   leaving their flocks, draw nigh with lowly fear;
   we too will thither bend our joyful footsteps:

4. Lo, star-led chieftains,
   Magi, Christ adoring,
   offer him incense, gold and myrrh;
   we to the Christ-child bring our hearts' oblations:

5. Child, for us sinners
   poor and in the manger,
   fain we embrace thee, with love and awe;
   who would not love thee, loving us so dearly?

6. Sing, choirs of angels,
   sing in exultation,
   sing, all ye citizens of heav'n above;
   glory to God in the highest:

7. Yea, Lord, we greet thee,
   born this happy morning,
   Jesu, to thee be glory giv'n;
   Word of the Father, now in flesh appearing:

Text: possibly by John Francis Wade (1711 - 1786) trans.
Frederick Oakeley (1802 - 1880) and others
Music: possibly by John Francis Wade (1711 - 1786)

3 Christians, awake!

YORKSHIRE (STOCKPORT) 10 10 10 10 10 10

1. Christ - ians, a - wake! sa - lute the hap - py morn, where - on the

C G7 C G7 C F C Dm7

Sa - viour of the world was born; rise to a - dore the

C G7 C G C F

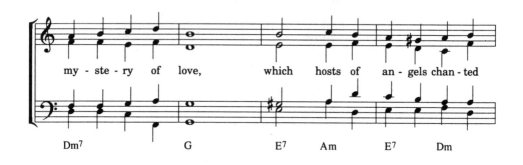

my - ste - ry of love, which hosts of an - gels chan - ted

Dm7 G E7 Am E7 Dm

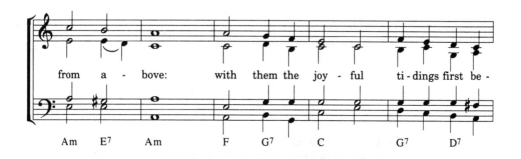

from a - bove: with them the joy - ful ti - dings first be -

Am E7 Am F G7 C G7 D7

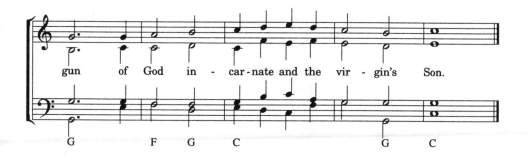

gun of God in - car - nate and the vir - gin's Son.

2. Then to the watchful shepherds it was told,
   who heard th' angelic herald's voice, 'Behold,
   I bring good tidings of a Saviour's birth
   to you and all the nations on the earth:
   this day hath God fulfilled his promised word,
   this day is born a Saviour, Christ the Lord.'

3. He spake; and straightway the celestial choir
   in hymns of joy, unknown before, conspire;
   the praises of redeeming love they sang,
   and heav'n's whole orb with alleluias rang:
   God's highest glory was their anthem still,
   peace on the earth, in ev'ry heart good will.

4. To Bethl'em straight th'enlightened shepherds ran,
   to see, unfolding, God's eternal plan,
   and found, with Joseph and the blessèd maid,
   her Son, the Saviour, in a manger laid:
   then to their flocks, still praising God, return,
   and their glad hearts with holy rapture burn.

5. O may we keep and ponder in our mind
   God's wondrous love in saving lost mankind;
   trace we the babe, who hath retrieved our loss,
   from his poor manger to his bitter cross;
   tread in his steps, assisted by his grace,
   till our first heav'nly state again takes place.

6. Then may we hope, th'angelic hosts among,
   to sing, redeemed, a glad triumphal song:
   he that was born upon this joyful day
   around us all his glory shall display;
   saved by his love, incessant we shall sing
   eternal praise to heav'n's almighty King.

Text: John Byrom (1692 - 1763) alt.
Music: John Wainwright (1723 - 1768)

4 The first Nowell

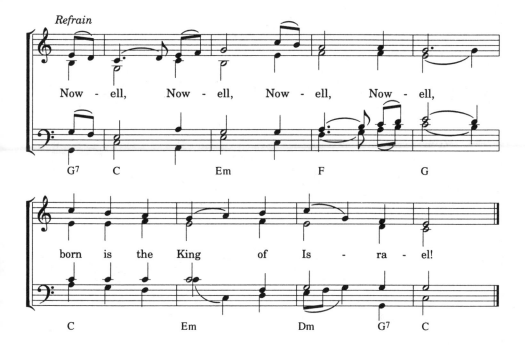

Refrain

Now - ell, Now - ell, Now - ell, Now - ell,

G⁷ C   Em   F   G

born is the King of Is - ra - el!

C   Em   Dm   G⁷ C

2. They lookèd up and saw a star,
   shining in the east, beyond them far,
   and to the earth it gave great light,
   and so it continued both day and night.

3. And by the light of that same star,
   three wise men came from country far;
   to seek for a king was their intent,
   and to follow the star wherever it went.

4. This star drew nigh to the north-west,
   o'er Bethlehem it took its rest,
   and there it did both stop and stay
   right over the place where Jesus lay.

5. Then entered in those wise men three,
   full rev'rently upon their knee,
   and offered there in his presence,
   their gold and myrrh and frankincense.

6. Then let us all with one accord
   sing praises to our heav'nly Lord,
   that hath made heav'n and earth of naught,
   and with his blood mankind hath bought.

Text: from William Sandys' *Christmas Carols, Ancient and Modern* (1833)
Music: traditional English melody arr. John Stainer (1840 - 1901)

5 Sing lullaby

THE INFANT KING 494 89 94

1. Sing lul - la - by! Lul - la - by ba - by, now re -
clin - ing, sing lul - la - by! Hush, do not wake the in - fant
king. An - gels are watch - ing, stars are shin - ing o - ver the
place where he is ly - ing: sing lul - la - by!

2. Sing lullaby!
   Lullaby baby, now a-sleeping,
   sing lullaby!
   Hush, do not wake the infant king.
   Soon will come sorrow with the morning,
   soon will come bitter grief and weeping:
   sing lullaby!

3. Sing lullaby!
   Lullaby baby, now a-dozing,
   sing lullaby!
   Hush, do not wake the infant king.
   Soon comes the cross, the nails, the piercing,
   then in the grave at last reposing:
   sing lullaby!

4. Sing lullaby!
   Lullaby! is the babe awaking?
   Sing lullaby.
   Hush, do not stir the infant king.
   Dreaming of Easter, gladsome morning,
   conquering death, its bondage breaking:
   sing lullaby!

Text: Sabine Baring-Gould (1834 - 1924)
Music: Old Basque Noël arr. Philip Moore (b. 1943)

6 What child is this

GREENSLEEVES 87 87 68 67

come, greet the in - fant Lord, the babe, the Son of Ma - ry!

G   D   Em   B⁷   Em

2. Why lies he in such mean estate,
   where ox and ass are feeding?
   Good Christians, fear: for sinners here
   the silent Word is pleading.
   Nails, spear, shall pierce him through,
   the cross be borne for me, for you:
   hail, hail the Word made flesh,
   the babe, the Son of Mary!

3. So bring him incense, gold and myrrh,
   come rich and poor, to own him.
   The King of kings salvation brings,
   let loving hearts enthrone him.
   Raise, raise the song on high,
   the Virgin sings her lullaby:
   joy, joy for Christ is born,
   the babe, the Son of Mary!

Text: William Chatterton Dix (1837 - 1898) alt.
Music: traditional English melody arr. John Stainer (1840 - 1901)

7 Away in a manger

CRADLE SONG 11 11 11 11

1. A-way in a man-ger, no crib for a bed, the lit-tle Lord Je-sus laid down his sweet head. The stars in the bright sky looked down where he lay, the lit-tle Lord Je-sus, a-sleep on the hay.

2. The cattle are lowing, the baby awakes,
   but little Lord Jesus no crying he makes.
   I love thee, Lord Jesus! Look down from the sky,
   and stay by my side until morning is nigh.

3. Be near me, Lord Jesus; I ask thee to stay
   close by me for ever, and love me, I pray.
   Bless all the dear children in thy tender care,
   and fit us for heaven, to live with thee there.

An alternative version of verses 2 and 3

2. The cattle are lowing, they also adore
the little Lord Jesus who lies in the straw.
I love you, Lord Jesus, I know you are near
to love and protect me till morning is here.

3. Be near me, Lord Jesus; I ask you to stay
close by me for ever, and love me, I pray.
Bless all the dear children in your tender care,
prepare us for heaven, to live with you there.

A unison arrangement

Original text: William James Kirkpatrick (1838 - 1921)
Alernative text, verses 2 and 3: Michael Forster (*b.* 1946)
Music: William James Kirkpatrick (1838 - 1921) arr. Richard Lloyd (*b.* 1933)

8 Born in the night, Mary's child

MARY'S CHILD 76 76

2. Clear shining light,
   Mary's child,
   your face lights up our way;
   light of the world,
   Mary's child,
   dawn on our darkened day.

3. Truth of our life,
   Mary's child,
   you tell us God is good;
   prove it is true,
   Mary's child,
   go to your cross of wood.

4. Hope of the world,
   Mary's child,
   you're coming soon to reign;
   King of the earth,
   Mary's child,
   walk in our streets again.

Text and music: Geoffrey Ainger (*b*. 1925)

9 Child in the manger

BUNESSAN 55 53 D

Unison 1. Child in the man - ger, in - fant of Ma - ry; out - cast and stran - ger, Lord of all; child who in - he - rits all our trans - gres - sions, all our de - me - rits on him fall.

2. Once the most holy child of salvation
   gently and lowly lived below;
   now as our glorious mighty Redeemer,
   see him victorious o'er each foe.

3. Prophets foretold him, infant of wonder;
   angels behold him on his throne;
   worthy our Saviour of all their praises;
   happy for ever are his own.

Text Mary MacDonald (1817 - 1890) trans. Lachlan MacBean (1853 - 1931)
Music: traditional Gaelic melody arr. Colin Hand (*b.* 1929)

10 God rest you merry, gentlemen

GOD REST YOU MERRY 86 86 86 and Refrain

Unison 1. God rest you mer-ry, gen-tle-men, let no-thing you dis-may, for

Je-sus Christ our Sa - viour was born on Christ-mas day, to

save us all from Sa - tan's pow'r when we were gone a-stray: *Refrain* O

ti - dings of com - fort and joy, com-fort and joy, O

2. In Bethlehem, in Jewry,
   this blessèd babe was born,
   and laid within a manger,
   upon this blessèd morn;
   the which his mother Mary
   did nothing take in scorn.

3. From God, our heav'nly Father,
   a blessèd angel came,
   and unto certain shepherds
   brought tidings of the same,
   how that in Bethlehem was born
   the Son of God by name.

4. 'Fear not,' then said the angel,
   'let nothing you affright,
   this day is born a Saviour,
   of virtue, pow'r and might;
   by him the world is overcome
   and Satan put to flight.'

5. The shepherds at those tidings
   rejoicèd much in mind,
   and left their flocks a-feeding,
   in tempest, storm and wind,
   and went to Bethlehem straightway
   this blessèd babe to find.

6. But when to Bethlehem they came,
   whereat this infant lay,
   they found him in a manger,
   where oxen feed on hay;
   his mother Mary kneeling,
   unto the Lord did pray.

7. Now to the Lord sing praises,
   all you within this place,
   and with true love and fellowship
   each other now embrace;
   this holy tide of Christmas
   all others doth deface.

Text: traditional English alt.
Music: traditional English melody arr. Adrian Vernon Fish (b. 1956)

11 Come, come, come to the manger

COME TO THE MANGER Irregular and Refrain

Refrain

Unison Come, come, come to the man - ger, chil - dren, come to the

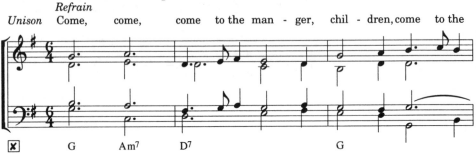

G   Am7   D7   G

chil - dren's King;   sing,   sing,   chor - us of an - gels,

C   D   G   A7   D

star of morn - ing o'er Beth - le - hem sing.   1. He lies 'mid the beasts of the

Fine

G   D7   G   Em

stall,   who is Ma - ker and Lord of us   all;   the

Am   D7   G   A7   D7

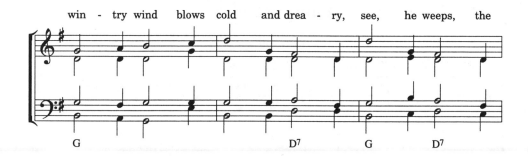

win - try wind blows cold and drea - ry, see, he weeps, the

G   D⁷   G   D⁷

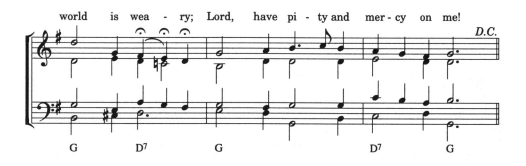

world is wea - ry; Lord, have pi - ty and mer - cy on me! *D.C.*

G   D⁷   G   D⁷   G

2. He leaves all his glory behind,
   to be born and to die for mankind,
   with grateful beasts his cradle chooses,
   thankless world his love refuses;
   Lord, have pity and mercy on me!

3. To the manger of Bethlehem come,
   to the Saviour Emmanuel's home;
   the heav'nly hosts above are singing,
   set the Christmas bells a-ringing;
   Lord, have pity and mercy on me!

Text: unknown, alt.
Music: traditional melody adapted by S. P. Waddington

12 A great and mighty wonder

ES IST EIN' ROS' ENTSPRUNGEN 76 76 676

1.A great and migh-ty won-der, a full and ho-ly cure!

The Vir-gin bears the in-fant with vir-gin-ho-nour pure:

Refrain

Re-peat the hymn a-gain! 'To God on high be

glo-ry, and peace on earth shall reign.'

2. The Word becomes incarnate,
and yet remains on high;
and cherubim sing anthems
to shepherds from the sky:

3. While thus they sing your monarch,
those bright angelic bands,
rejoice, ye vales and mountains,
ye oceans, clap your hands:

4. Since all he comes to ransom
by all be he adored,
the infant born in Bethl'em,
the Saviour and the Lord:

Text: St. Germanus (*c.* 634 - *c.* 734) trans. John Mason Neale (1818 - 1866)
Music: German carol melody, harmonies based on Michael Praetorius (1571 - 1621) alt.

13 Good Christians all, rejoice

IN DULCI JUBILO Irregular

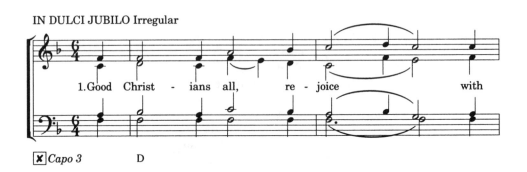

1. Good Christ - ians all, re - joice with

☒ Capo 3   D

heart and soul and voice! Give ye heed to

A⁷

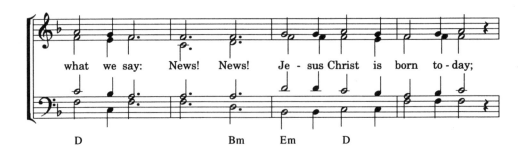

what we say: News! News! Je - sus Christ is born to - day;

D   Bm   Em   D

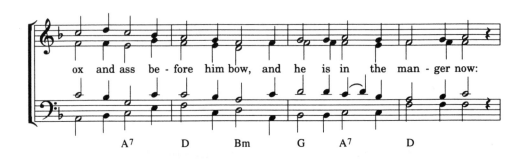

ox and ass be - fore him bow, and he is in the man - ger now:

A⁷   D   Bm   G   A⁷   D

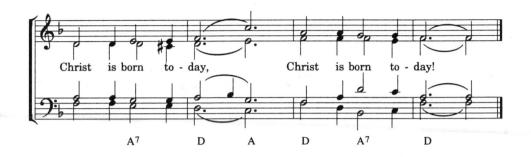

Christ is born to - day, Christ is born to - day!

A⁷   D   A   D   A⁷   D

2. Good Christians all, rejoice
with heart and soul and voice!
Now ye hear of endless bliss:
Joy! Joy! Jesus Christ was born for this.
He hath opened heaven's door,
and we are blest for evermore:
Christ was born for this,
Christ was born for this.

3. Good Christians all, rejoice
with heart and soul and voice!
Now ye need not fear the grave:
Peace! Peace! Jesus Christ was born to save;
calls you one, and calls you all,
to gain his everlasting hall:
Christ was born to save,
Christ was born to save.

Text: John Mason Neale (1818 - 1866) alt.
Music: 14th century German carol melody arr. John Stainer (1840 - 1901)

14 Angels from the realms of glory

IRIS 87 87 and Refrain

1. Angels, from the realms of glory,
wing your flight o'er all the earth;
ye who sang creation's story
now proclaim Messiah's birth:

Refrain
Come and

Capo 3 D · A⁷ · D · Bm · A⁷ · D · A⁷ · D · Bm · A⁷ · D · D · B⁷ · Em · A⁷ · D · G

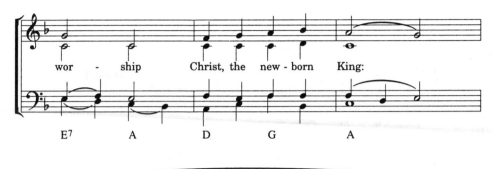

wor - ship Christ, the new-born King:

E⁷   A   D   G   A

come   and

D   B⁷   Em   A⁷   D   G

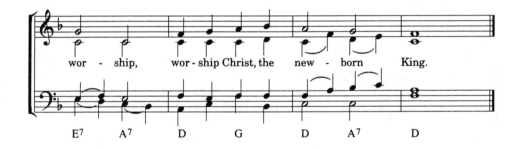

wor - ship,   wor - ship Christ, the new - born King.

E⁷   A⁷   D   G   D   A⁷   D

2. Shepherds, in the field abiding,
   watching o'er your flocks by night,
   God with us is now residing,
   yonder shines the infant Light:

3. Sages, leave your contemplations;
   brighter visions beam afar:
   seek the great Desire of Nations;
   ye have seen his natal star:

4. Saints before the altar bending,
   watching long in hope and fear,
   suddenly the Lord, descending,
   in his temple shall appear:

5. Though an infant now we view him,
   he shall fill his Father's throne,
   gather all the nations to him;
   ev'ry knee shall then bow down:

Text: James Montgomery (1771 - 1854)
Music: French or Flemish melody arr. Richard Lloyd (b. 1933)

15 Hark, the herald-angels sing

MENDELSSOHN 77 77 D and Refrain

1. Hark, the he - rald - an - gels sing glo - ry to the new - born King; peace on earth and mer - cy mild, God and sin - ners re - con - ciled: joy - ful, all ye na - tions rise, join the tri - umph of the skies, with th'an - ge - lic host pro - claim, 'Christ is born in Beth - le - hem.'

Capo 3 D A⁷ D A E⁷ A D G A⁷ D G A⁷ G B⁷ Em A⁷ D A⁷ D

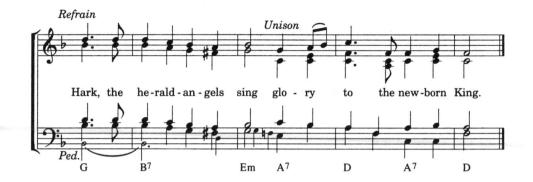

Refrain

Hark, the he-rald-an-gels sing glo-ry to the new-born King.

G   B⁷   Em   A⁷   D   A⁷   D

2. Christ, by highest heav'n adored,
   Christ, the everlasting Lord,
   late in time behold him come,
   offspring of a virgin's womb!
   Veiled in flesh the Godhead see,
   hail, th'incarnate Deity!
   Pleased as man with us to dwell,
   Jesus, our Emmanuel.

3. Hail, the heav'n-born Prince of Peace!
   Hail, the Sun of Righteousness!
   Light and life to all he brings,
   ris'n with healing in his wings;
   mild he lays his glory by,
   born that we no more may die,
   born to raise us from the earth,
   born to give us second birth.

Text: Charles Wesley (1707 - 1788), George Whitefield (1714 - 1770),
Martin Madan (1726 - 1790) and others, alt.
Music: adapted from Felix Mendelssohn (1809 - 1847)
by William Hayman Cummings (1831 - 1915)

16 The Virgin Mary had a baby boy

This arrangement © Copyright 1994 Kevin Mayhew Ltd.

2. The angels sang when the baby was born, (3)
   and proclaimed him the Saviour Jesus.

3. The wise men saw where the baby was born, (3)
   and they saw that his name was Jesus.

Text: traditional West Indian
Music: traditional West Indian arr. Christopher Tambling (*b*. 1964)

17 Ding dong! merrily on high

BRANLE DE L'OFFICIAL 77 77 and Refrain

1. Ding dong! mer-ri-ly on high, in heav'n the bells are ring - ing;
ding dong! ve-ri-ly the sky is riv'n with an-gel-sing - ing.

Glo - - - ri - a, ho-san-na in ex-cel-sis!

Text and arrangement © Copyright revived 1996.
Alternative Refrain © Copyright 1994 Kevin Mayhew Ltd.

2. E'en so here below, below,
   let steeple bells be swungen,
   and io, io, io,
   by priest and people sungen.

3. Pray you, dutifully prime
   your matin chime, ye ringers;
   may you beautifully rhyme
   your evetime song, ye singers.

An alternative setting of the refrain

Text: George Ratcliffe Woodward (1848 - 1934)
Music: traditional French melody arr. Charles Wood (1866 - 1926)
alternative Refrain arr. Colin Hand (b. 1929)

18 Joy to the world

ANTIOCH CM

1. Joy to the world! The Lord is come; let earth re-ceive her
King; let ev - 'ry heart pre - pare him room and
heav'n and na - ture sing, and heav'n and na - ture sing, and
heav'n, and heav'n and na - ture sing!

and heav'n and na - ture sing,
and heav'n and na - ture
sing,

2. Joy to the earth! The Saviour reigns;
   let us our songs employ;
   while fields and floods, rocks, hills and plains
   repeat the sounding joy,
   repeat the sounding joy,
   repeat, repeat the sounding joy.

3. He rules the world with truth and grace,
   and makes the nations prove
   the glories of his righteousness,
   and wonders of his love,
   and wonders of his love,
   and wonders, and wonders of his love.

A lower setting

1. Joy to the world! The Lord is come; let earth re-ceive her King; let ev-'ry heart pre-pare him room and heav'n and na-ture sing, and heav'n and na-ture sing, and and heav'n and na-ture sing, and heav'n and na-ture heav'n, and heav'n and na-ture sing! sing,

Text: Isaac Watts (1674 - 1748) alt.
Music: George Frideric Handel (1685 - 1759)

19 Little Jesus, sweetly sleep

ROCKING 10 7 88 77

1. Little Jesus, sweetly sleep, do not stir; we will lend a coat of fur; we will rock you, rock you, rock you, we will rock you, rock you, rock you; see the fur to keep you warm,

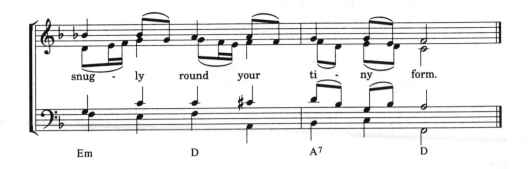

snug - ly round your ti - ny form.

Em   D   A⁷   D

2. Mary's little baby sleep, sweetly sleep,
   sleep in comfort, slumber deep;
   we will rock you, rock you, rock you,
   we will rock you, rock you, rock you;
   we will serve you all we can,
   darling, darling little man.

Text: traditional Czech carol trans. Percy Dearmer (1867 - 1936)
Music: Czech carol collected by Martin Shaw arr. Christopher Tambling (b. 1964)

20 O little town of Bethlehem (Tune 1)

FOREST GREEN DCM

2. For Christ is born of Mary;
   and, gathered all above,
   while mortals sleep, the angels keep
   their watch of wond'ring love;
   O morning stars, together
   proclaim the holy birth,
   and praises sing to God the King,
   and peace upon the earth.

3. How silently, how silently,
   the wondrous gift is giv'n!
   So God imparts to human hearts
   the blessings of his heav'n.
   No ear may hear his coming;
   but in this world of sin,
   where meek souls will receive him still,
   the dear Christ enters in.

4. O holy child of Bethlehem,
   descend to us, we pray;
   cast out our sin, and enter in,
   be born in us today.
   We hear the Christmas angels
   the great glad tidings tell:
   O come to us, abide with us,
   our Lord Emmanuel.

Text: Phillips Brooks (1835 - 1893) alt.
Music: traditional English melody collected and arr. Ralph Vaughan Williams (1872 - 1958)

21 O little town of Bethlehem (Tune 2)

CHRISTMAS CAROL DCM

1. O lit - tle town of Beth - le - hem, how still we see thee

Capo 3   A   D   A⁷   D   G   D

lie! A - bove thy deep and dream - less sleep the

F♯m   A⁷   D   A   D

si - lent stars go by. Yet in thy dark streets

A⁷   C♯⁷   F♯m   C♯⁷   F♯m

shi - neth the e - ver - last - ing light; the hopes and fears of

C♯⁷   F♯m   E⁷   A   A⁷   D

all the years are met in thee to - night.

Bm   D   G   D   F#m   A   D

2. For Christ is born of Mary;
   and, gathered all above,
   while mortals sleep, the angels keep
   their watch of wond'ring love;
   O morning stars, together
   proclaim the holy birth,
   and praises sing to God the King,
   and peace upon the earth.

3. How silently, how silently,
   the wondrous gift is giv'n!
   So God imparts to human hearts
   the blessings of his heav'n.
   No ear may hear his coming;
   but in this world of sin,
   where meek souls will receive him still,
   the dear Christ enters in.

4. O holy child of Bethlehem,
   descend to us, we pray;
   cast out our sin, and enter in,
   be born in us today.
   We hear the Christmas angels
   the great glad tidings tell:
   O come to us, abide with us,
   our Lord Emmanuel.

Text: Phillips Brooks (1835 - 1893) alt.
Music: Henry Walford Davies (1869 - 1941)

22 The angel Gabriel from heaven came

BIRJINA GAZTETTOBAT ZEGOEN 10 10 12 10

2. 'For known a blessèd Mother thou shalt be.
   All generations laud and honour thee.
   Thy Son shall be Emmanuel, by seers foretold,
   most highly favoured lady.' Gloria!

3. Then gentle Mary meekly bowed her head.
   'To me be as it pleaseth God,' she said.
   'My soul shall laud and magnify his holy name.'
   Most highly favoured lady! Gloria!

4. Of her, Emmanuel, the Christ, was born
   in Bethlehem, all on a Christmas morn;
   and Christian folk throughout the world will ever say:
   'Most highly favoured lady.' Gloria!

Text: Sabine Baring-Gould (1834 - 1924)
Music: traditional Basque melody arr. Richard Lloyd (b. 1933)

23 Once in royal David's city

IRBY 87 87 77

1. Once in roy - al Da - vid's ci - ty stood a
low - ly cat - tle shed, where a mo - ther laid her
ba - by in a man - ger for his bed: Ma - ry
was that mo - ther mild, Je - sus Christ her lit - tle child.

2. He came down to earth from heaven,
   who is God and Lord of all,
   and his shelter was a stable,
   and his cradle was a stall;
   with the poor and mean and lowly,
   lived on earth our Saviour holy.

3. And through all his wondrous childhood
   day by day like us he grew;
   he was little, weak and helpless,
   tears and smiles like us he knew;
   and he feeleth for our sadness,
   and he shareth in our gladness.

4. Still among the poor and lowly
   hope in Christ is brought to birth,
   with the promise of salvation
   for the nations of the earth;
   still in him our life is found
   and our hope of heav'n is crowned.

5. And our eyes at last shall see him
   through his own redeeming love,
   for that child so dear and gentle
   is our Lord in heav'n above;
   and he leads his children on
   to the place where he is gone.

Text: vs. 1-3 and 5: Cecil Frances Alexander (1818 - 1895) alt.
v. 4: Michael Forster (b. 1946)
Music: Henry John Gauntlett (1805 - 1876)

24 Unto us a boy is born

PUER NOBIS 76 77

2. Cradled in a stall was he,
   watched by cows and asses;
   but the very beasts could see
   that he the world surpasses,
   that he the world surpasses.

3. Then the fearful Herod cried,
   'Pow'r is mine in Jewry!'
   So the blameless children died
   the victims of his fury,
   the victims of his fury.

4. Now may Mary's Son, who came
   long ago to love us,
   lead us all with hearts aflame
   unto the joys above us,
   unto the joys above us.

5. Omega and Alpha he!
   Let the organ thunder,
   while the choir with peals of glee
   shall rend the air asunder,
   shall rend the air asunder.

Text: 15th century trans. Percy Dearmer (1867 - 1936) alt.
Music: from *Piae Cantiones* (1582) arr. Adrian Vernon Fish (*b.* 1956)

25 Love came down at Christmas

LOVE CAME DOWN 67 67

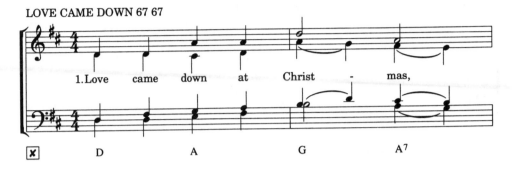

1. Love came down at Christ - mas,

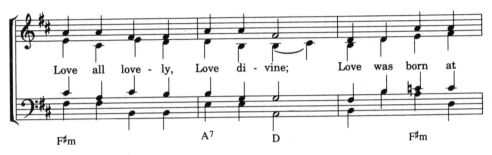

Love all love - ly, Love di - vine; Love was born at

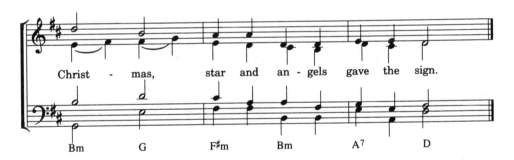

Christ - mas, star and an - gels gave the sign.

2. Worship we the Godhead,
   Love incarnate, Love divine;
   worship we our Jesus:
   but wherewith for sacred sign?

3. Love shall be our token,
   love be yours and love be mine,
   love to God and all men,
   love for plea and gift and sign.

Text: Christina Georgina Rossetti (1830 - 1894)
Music: Malcolm Archer (b. 1952)
Music © Copyright 1991 Kevin Mayhew Ltd

26 On Christmas night all Christians sing

SUSSEX CAROL 88 88 88

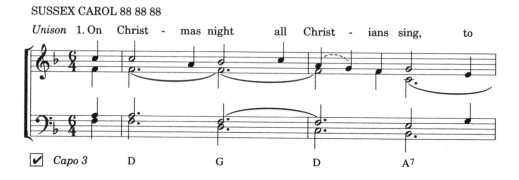

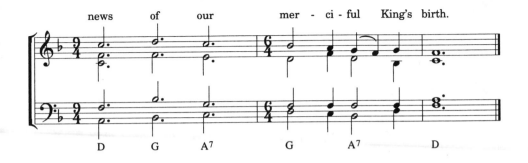

2. Then why should we on earth be so sad,
   since our Redeemer made us glad,
   then why should we on earth be so sad,
   since our Redeemer made us glad,
   when from our sin he set us free,
   all for to gain our liberty?

3. When sin departs before his grace,
   then life and health come in its place,
   when sin departs before his grace,
   then life and health come in its place,
   angels and earth with joy may sing,
   all for to see the new-born King.

4. All out of darkness we have light,
   which made the angels sing this night:
   all out of darkness we have light,
   which made the angels sing this night:
   'Glory to God and peace to men,
   now and for evermore. Amen.'

Text: traditional English carol alt.
Music: traditional English melody collected and arr. Ralph Vaughan Williams (1872 - 1958)

27 While shepherds watched

WINCHESTER OLD CM

1. While shep - herds watched their flocks by night, all
seat - ed on the ground, the an - gel of the
Lord came down, and glo - ry shone a - round.

Capo 3

D   G   D
Bm   E7   A7   D7   G
A   F♯m   G   A7   D

2. 'Fear not,' said he (for mighty dread
   had seized their troubled mind);
   'glad tidings of great joy I bring
   to you and all mankind.

3. 'To you in David's town this day
   is born of David's line
   a Saviour, who is Christ the Lord;
   and this shall be the sign:

4. 'The heav'nly babe you there shall find
to human view displayed,
all meanly wrapped in swathing bands,
and in a manger laid.'

5. Thus spake the seraph, and forthwith
appeared a shining throng
of angels praising God, who thus
addressed their joyful song:

6. 'All glory be to God on high,
and to the earth be peace;
good will henceforth from heav'n to men
begin and never cease.'

A lower setting

1. While shepherds watched their flocks by night, all seated on the ground, the angel of the Lord came down, and glory shone around.

Text: Nahum Tate (1652 - 1715)
Music: from Thomas Este's *Psalter* (1592)

28 O little one sweet, O little one mild

O JESULEIN SÜSS 10 9 88 10

1. O lit - tle one sweet, O lit - tle one mild, thy
Fa - ther's pur - pose thou hast ful - filled; thou cam'st from
heav'n to dwell be - low, to share the joys and
tears we know. O lit - tle one sweet, O lit - tle one mild.

2. O little one sweet, O little one mild,
with joy thou hast the whole world filled;
thou camest here from heav'n's domain,
to bring us comfort in our pain,
O little one sweet, O little one mild.

3. O little one sweet, O little one mild,
in thee Love's beauties are all distilled;
then light in us thy love's bright flame,
that we may give thee back the same,
O little one sweet, O little one mild.

Text: German, Samuel Scheidt (1650) trans. Percy Dearmer (1867 - 1936) alt.
Music: melody from Samuel Scheidt's *Tabulaturbuch* (1650) harmonised by
Martin Shaw (1875 - 1958)

Another harmonisation

1. O lit - tle one sweet, O lit - tle one mild, thy Fa - ther's pur - pose thou hast ful - filled; thou cam'st from heav'n to dwell be - low, to share the joys and tears we know, O lit - tle one sweet, O lit - tle one mild.

This harmony: Johann Sebastian Bach (1685 - 1750)

29 The holly and the ivy

Unison 1. The hol-ly and the i-vy, when they are both full grown, of all the trees that are in the wood the hol-ly bears the crown.

D Bm A

D Bm G A⁷ D

Refrain The ri-sing of the sun and the run-ning of the deer, the

Bm A⁷

play-ing of the mer-ry or-gan, sweet sing-ing in the choir.

D Bm G A⁷ D

☒ *Capo 3*

2. The holly bears a blossom,
white as the lily flow'r,
and Mary bore sweet Jesus Christ
to be our sweet Saviour.

3. The holly bears a berry,
as red as any blood,
and Mary bore sweet Jesus Christ
to do poor sinners good.

4. The holly bears a prickle,
   as sharp as any thorn,
   and Mary bore sweet Jesus Christ
   on Christmas day in the morn.

5. The holly bears a bark,
   as bitter as any gall,
   and Mary bore sweet Jesus Christ
   for to redeem us all.

6. The holly and the ivy,
   when they are both full grown,
   of all the trees that are in the wood
   the holly bears the crown.

A lower setting

Text: traditional
Music: English folk carol arr. Adrian Vernon Fish (*b.* 1956)

30 Of the Father's love begotten

CORDE NATUS (DIVINUM MYSTERIUM) 87 87 87 7

Unison 1. Of the Fa - ther's love be - got - ten,

ⓧ *Capo 3*   C   F   G⁷   Am

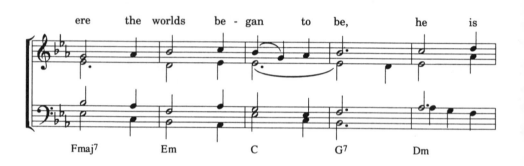

ere the worlds be - gan to be, he is

Fmaj⁷   Em   C   G⁷   Dm

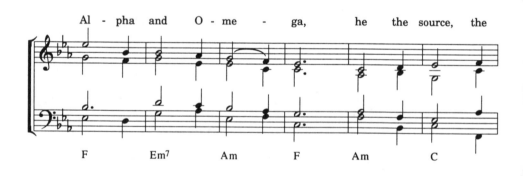

Al - pha and O - me - ga, he the source, the

F   Em⁷   Am   F   Am   C

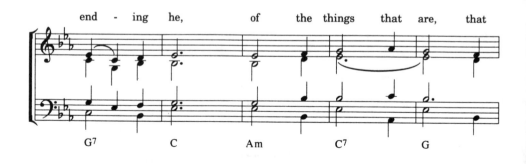

end - ing he, of the things that are, that

G⁷   C   Am   C⁷   G

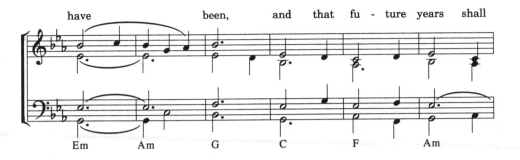

have been, and that fu-ture years shall

Em Am G C F Am

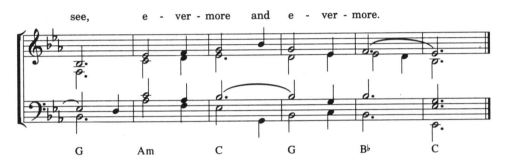

see, e-ver-more and e-ver-more.

G Am C G B♭ C

2. At his word they were created;
   he commanded; it was done:
   heav'n and earth and depths of ocean
   in their threefold order one;
   all that grows beneath the shining
   of the light of moon and sun,
   evermore and evermore.

3. O that birth for ever blessèd,
   when the Virgin, full of grace,
   by the Holy Ghost conceiving,
   bare the Saviour of our race,
   and the babe, the world's Redeemer,
   first revealed his sacred face,
   evermore and evermore.

4. O ye heights of heav'n, adore him;
   angel hosts, his praises sing;
   pow'rs, dominions, bow before him,
   and extol our God and King:
   let no tongue on earth be silent,
   ev'ry voice in concert ring,
   evermore and evermore.

5. This is he whom seers and sages
   sang of old with one accord;
   whom the writings of the prophets
   promised in their faithful word;
   now he shines, the long-expected:
   let our songs declare his worth,
   evermore and evermore.

6. Christ, to thee, with God the Father,
   and, O Holy Ghost, to thee,
   hymn and chant and high thanksgiving,
   and unwearied praises be;
   honour, glory, and dominion,
   and eternal victory,
   evermore and evermore.

Text: Aurelius Clemens Prudentius (348 - 413) trans. John Mason Neale (1818 - 1866) alt.
Music: Plainsong melody adapted by Theodoricus Petrus in *Piae Cantiones* (1582)

31 See amid the winter's snow

HUMILITY (OXFORD) 77 77 and Refrain

Unison 1. See a - mid the win - ter's snow, born for us on

earth be - low, see the ten - der Lamb ap - pears,

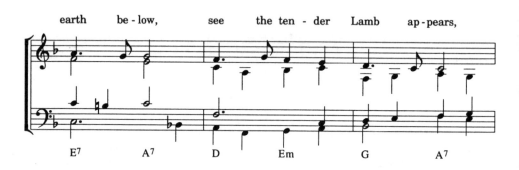

prom - ised from e - ter - nal years. Hail, thou e - ver -

Refrain
Harmony

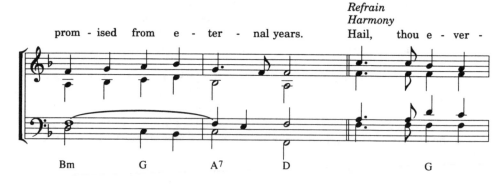

bles - sed morn, hail, re - demp - tion's hap - py dawn!

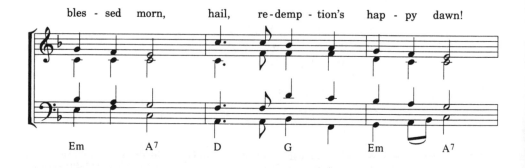

Sing through all Je - ru - sa - lem, Christ is born in Beth - le - hem.

D   E⁷   A⁷   D   G   A⁷   D

2. Lo, within a manger lies
   he who built the starry skies;
   he who, throned in heights sublime,
   sits amid the cherubim.

3. Say, ye holy shepherds, say,
   what your joyful news today?
   Wherefore have ye left your sheep
   on the lonely mountain steep?

4. 'As we watched at dead of night,
   lo, we saw a wondrous light;
   angels, singing peace on earth,
   told us of the Saviour's birth.'

5. Sacred infant, all divine,
   what a tender love was thine,
   thus to come from highest bliss,
   down to such a world as this!

6. Virgin mother, Mary blest,
   by the joys that fill thy breast,
   pray for us, that we may prove
   worthy of the Saviour's love.

Text: Edward Caswall (1814 - 1878)
Music: John Goss (1800 - 1880)

32 Silent night

STILLE NACHT Irregular

1. Si - lent night, ho - ly night. All is calm,
all is bright, round yon vir - gin mo - ther and child;
ho - ly in - fant, so ten - der and mild, sleep in hea - ven - ly
peace, sleep in hea - ven - ly peace.

Capo 3 G

Am⁷ D⁷

G G⁷ C G

C Am D⁷ G Am⁷ D⁷

G D⁷ G

2. Silent night, holy night.
   Shepherds quake at the sight,
   glories stream from heaven afar,
   heav'nly hosts sing alleluia:
   Christ, the Saviour is born,
   Christ, the Saviour is born.

3. Silent night, holy night.
   Son of God, love's pure light,
   radiant beams from thy holy face,
   with the dawn of redeeming grace:
   Jesus, Lord, at thy birth,
   Jesus, Lord, at thy birth.

Text: Joseph Mohr (1792 - 1848) trans. John Freeman Young (1820 - 1885)
Music: Franz Grüber (1787 - 1863) arr. Colin Hand (b. 1929)